Mr Peek's Poetry Fun time

Volume 1

BITS & BOBS
From
Mr Peek's Poetry Place

www.mrpeekspoetryplace.co.uk

BORROWED BOOKS

First published in 2016 by Borrowed Books Hastings, UK.
Printed in China by Gold Printing.

A CIP record for this book is available from the British Library

ISBN

978-953-6374-96-0

Contents

Bits & Bobs

Reading Books

Inside each book there is a world
Between the letters it's been curled,

And when you read a book with me
That world comes out for us to see.

Then you and I can travel there
And in this world we both can share.

So come and sit with me a while,
Please read for me and make me smile

Let's open up and take a look
Inside this magic,
Reading book.

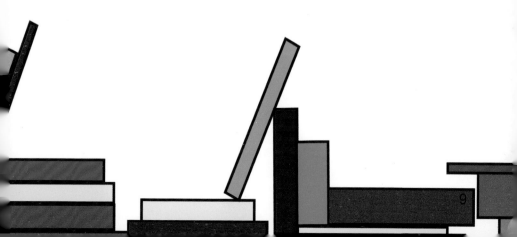

Clap Your Hands!

Clap your hands!
Clap your hands!
Shake your body,
Stamp your feet.
I tell you all that exercise
Is really quite a treat!

Jump around!
Jump around!
Jump up high,
And come back down.
You know that when you're laughing
It's impossible to frown!

Dance about!
Dance about!
Do the shimmy,
Scream and shout.
I tell you all that fun and games
Is what life's all about!

Happy - Sad

If I am sad
For a short while,
I think good thoughts
And then I smile.

River Rhyme

By the river Severn
I counted to eleven,
And by the river Torridge
I ate a bowl of porridge.

By the river Tees
I washed my dirty knees,
And by the river Lune
I sang a little tune.

By the river Gipping
I couldn't keep from skipping,
And by the river Thame
I had to do the same.

I swam the river Rother
Without the slightest bother,
But as I crossed the Dee
I got washed out to sea!

Frosty Cold

When the weather's
Frosty cold
No-one does
What they've been told.
So all the teachers
Scream and shout
And put their gloves on
Inside out.

But
When the weather's
Warm and hot
Then no one does
What they should not.
So all the teachers
Smile instead
And put their knickers
On their head!

The Hungry Dinosaurs

So hungry were the dinosaurs
When they came into the house,
They ate up all the knives and forks
And then they ate the mouse.

Then they went around the bend
And ate up all the stairs,
And when they'd eaten all of them
They ate up all the chairs.

Well next they ate the TV
The bookshelves and a pram,
And afterwards made sandwiches
Of buttered bread and jam.

"Get out of here you dinosaurs!"
I screamed and made a fuss.
"Get out of here this minute,
And please leave some food for us."

The Sauropods

When the sauropods are coming
Then the ground begins to shake,
Can you hear the terrible, terrible
Terrible noise they make?
With feet the size of motor cars
And legs the size of trees,
They're walking through the forest
With their great big wobbly knees.

The sauropods, the sauropods
Diplodocus and his friends,
Imagine sliding from his head
To where his tail it ends.
Imagine being mistaken
For a tasty leafy treat,
Imagine being sat upon,
Or squashed beneath his feet.

The sauropods look wonderful
In all the books I know,
But if we travelled back in time
Would it be good to go?
Because maybe they're a bit too big
And not as friendly as they seem,
And if we met them in real life
We might just want to scream.

I am a little circle I'm very round and smart you know I always end up exactly where I start

16

The Ants! The Ants!

The Ants! The Ants!
They're marching
All across the forest floor.
They're carrying bits of leaves and fruits
And twigs and plenty more.
They carry them into the nest
And pack them in the store,
Where they feed the hungry fungus
That's the food they all adore.

The Ants! The Ants!
There's billions of them
Walking in the trees
And round the other animals
And tickling their knees.
They jumped on the orangutan
Then on the chimpanzees
And when they met the jaguar
They made him want to sneeze.

The Ants! The Ants!
They're marching so
You'd better get out of the way
They're cleaning up the forest floor
And they don't have time to play.
They're hurrying and scurrying
They're working night and day
And if they think you're tasty
Then they'll carry you away.

The Sounds I Love

The sounds I love, the sounds I love,
I love them all you know.
I love to hear the rain
Or hear the silence of the snow.
I love to hear a happy laugh,
I love when music's loud,
I love to hear the roar and cheer
Of a happy football crowd.

The sounds I love, the sounds I love,
Around me everyday,
The noise of pouring water,
Or the leaves I kick away,
The sound of drummers drumming,
Or Lego in a box,
Or late at night, when I'm awake,
The barking of a fox.

The sounds I love, the sounds I love,
Don't you just love them too?
And which of all the sounds we have,
Are the ones loved most by you?

Eating Flowers

I'm sitting in the garden
Eating lots of flowers,
I can sit and eat them all
For hours and hours and hours.

And when I'm feeling really full
I rush up to the loo,
And do a little wee-wee
And have a great big poo.

Daisy Dormouse

Daisy Dormouse snored and snored,
She snored so much
She almost roared,
When she woke up
She just felt bored.

So she slept and slept and slept
And all the animals she kept,
Awake all night
In such a fright
Because they thought a tiger bright
Was roaring, roaring,
In the night.

But the roar was not a tiger bright,
Just Daisy Dormouse,
In the night,
Boring, snoring,
Sleeping tight,
And dreaming of
A tiger's bite,
That gave her such
A dreadful fright
She roared just like
A tiger might
Out in the scary
Forest night.

Angry Auntie Antonella

Angry Auntie Antonella
Ate the top of an umbrella
Ate a sundial and a heater
And a rusty water meter.

Angry Auntie Antonella,
Ate six eggs with salmonella
Ate her bedroom and a mouse
Then she swallowed up her house.

Angry Auntie Antonella
Buttered sunshine with Nutella,
Ate a wind-chime and some rain
And a great big weather-vane.

Angry Auntie Antonella
Ate a hurricane called Stella
Ate the moon and stars for fun
And all the planets one by one.

Angry Auntie Antonella
Big and tall and interstellar
Ate the sun like it was cake
But then she made
A HUGE mistake...
In the dark,
With no food on her shelf,
My Angry Auntie ate...

Herself!

21

Don't Wake Me Up

When I sleep
My head is full
Of funny things
That kick and pull.

Like boxes that can play guitars
And yellow birds that come from Mars.
There's one legged goats that like to sing
And three-legged birds that all say "Ping!"
There's elephants that pull down trees
And fish that all have dirty knees.
There's floating bits of jammy toast,
And flying eggs that like to boast.
There's monkeys and Orangutans
And cardboard boxes that have fans.

Yes, when I sleep I see these things
And sometimes all of them have wings.

But when I wake,
As plain as day...
All these strange things
Have gone away.

Fish Wish

Inside a glass of orange juice
There swam a little fish
Who said that if I sang for him
He would grant me a wish,
And so I sang a little song
About a little fish,
Who swam around in orange juice
And granted me a wish.

Inside a glass of orange juice
There swam a little fish
Who said that if I danced for him
He would grant me a wish,
And so I did a little dance
About a little fish,
Who swam around in orange juice
And granted me a wish.

Inside a glass of orange juice
There swam a little fish
Who said that if I told a joke
He would grant me a wish,
And so I told a little joke
About a little fish,
Who swam around in orange juice
And granted me a wish.

The little fish he granted
Me wishes one, two, three
And then politely asked
If I could set him free,
And so I poured the orange juice
Out into the sea,
And then the little fish he
Waved goodbye to me.

23

Happy's Here To Stay

My friend called Mr Happy
He is a little clown,
And when he plays the mandolin
He plays it upside down.
But when he plays the banjo
He plays it on his head,
Unless he's laughing too much
Then he plays it in his bed.

My friend called Mr Happy
Sometimes he gets quite sad,
But then he eats some cherry pie
Which always makes him glad.
And when Mr Happy's happy
He dances in the hay,
And sings a little song for us
Called *Happy's here to stay*.

The Friend Ship

The friend ship sails upon the sea,
And makes us smile, my friends and me.
We laugh and joke,
And mess about.
We run and jump,
And scream and shout.

The friend ship is a happy place
Where I see smiles on every face.
But you know,
I really think,
Without my friends,
This ship would sink.

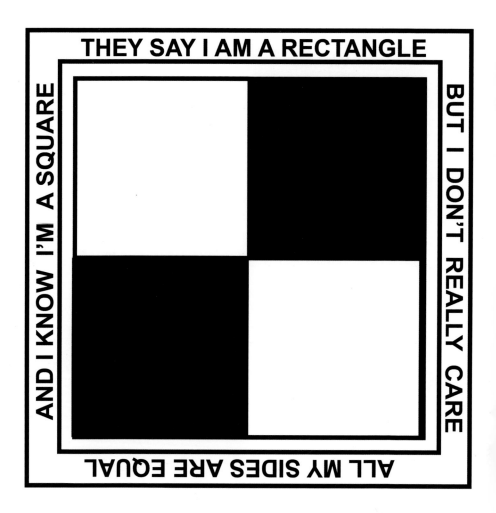

THEY SAY I AM A RECTANGLE

BUT I DON'T REALLY CARE

AND I KNOW I'M A SQUARE

ALL MY SIDES ARE EQUAL

The Sleepy Ghost

There was a sleepy little ghost
With worries in his head,
Because he thought a scary ghost
Was underneath his bed.

And so he moved and went to sleep
In the place he loved the most,
Underneath the creaky bed
Of another sleepy ghost.

Simon And The Rain

Simon is a happy man
He loves the sun and heat
He loves to eat potatoes
And he loves to rub his feet.
He loves to eat baked beans in bed
He loves to count his toes
He loves to do the jitterbug
While blowing on his nose.

Simon is the strangest man
That you will ever see
He loves to sit on ginger bread
While watching his TV.
But what makes Simon happiest
Again, again, again
Is to dance with his umbrella
Underneath the summer rain.

Silent Poem!

I'm going to write a poem,
Without a single sound,
No onomatopoeia,
No words that I have found.

I will not say the word,
That's spelt B A N G
Nor will I let you hear the sounds
I have inside of me.

No **CRASH! CLANG! WALLOP!**
No **SMASH! BONG! BING!**
No silly, silly noises
That just don't mean a thing.

I will not say GAZINGAR!
Or shout **BALANGAPOOP!**

Nor will I stand up on a chair
And scream WALLANGABOOP!
I will not go crazy
And start marching round the room,
Shouting in my loudest voice
CALAMITY! BOOM! BOOM!

No, I do not like such silly things,
I'm serious you know,
And if anyone starts being silly,
Then I think they'd better **GO!**

Ogg

A stone age man whose name was Ogg,
Was the first to train a dog.
He taught him how to hunt and walk
Then tried to teach him how to talk.
But as you know, and books they tell,
Dogs do not talk so very well.
So poor old Ogg was bound to fail...
All his dog did
Was wag its tail.

Yet still the dog and Ogg were good,
Their friendship worked out like it should.
The dog learnt how to hunt and fight
And kept guard over Ogg at night.
The dog was comfort and a friend
So much so, that in the end
All those that saw the great man Ogg,
Went out and got,
Themselves a dog.

So now, when you walk in the street
And see a dog at someone's feet.
Then spare a thought for good old Ogg,
The first man ever,
To train a dog.

Doctor! Doctor!

Doctor, doctor
I lelp me quick
You see I'm feeling really sick.
My skin's gone green
And shiny too,
My tongue feels
Just as big,
As you.

My eyes they bulge,
My hair is gone
I walk around
With nothing on.
My legs have grown,
And when I hop
I jump so hard
I just can't stop.

I feel like croaking
On a log,
I think I've turned,
Into a
Frog!

Awake

Let's both stay awake tonight,
Me and you in bed,
I don't really want to sleep,
Let's stay awake instead.

Let's not even close our eyes
Or lie still and relax,
Let's not let our brains turn off,
As we think of some facts.

Let's not drift off into dreams,
Or fill our heads with thought,
Let's not even think about,
The sleep fish we have caught.

Let's not sleep at all tonight,
Or even close our eyes,
Let's not dream of flying high,
Way up in the skies.

Let's lie in bed and wide awake
And wide awake let's keep.
And then I bet that suddenly,
We'll both be fast asleep.

Doctor! Doctor!

Doctor, doctor
Help me quick
You see I'm feeling really sick.
My tongue's gone rough,
My skin's grown fur,
And I can't speak anymore...
I purr.

I really want
To climb in trees
And suddenly
I've got four knees.
I've got long nails
(they're almost claws)
And really sharp teeth
In my jaws.
All I want
Is fish and milk
My fur's so smooth
It feels like silk.

What would you do
If I said that...
I think I've turned
Into a

Cat!

The Light And Dark

I have one hand
It cannot clap,
All it does
Is fall and flap.
But when one hand
It becomes two,
Then clap I can,
And clap I do.

I can play tennis
On my own,
But that's just stupid,
All alone,
And tennis is
So much more fun
When you play,
Against someone.

A candle burning,
Gives off light
That best can be seen,
In the night.
If candles just burn
In the day,
Then sunlight lights their light away.

A rainy day
Though not much fun,
Helps us appreciate
The sun.
For in life it's opposing things
That give us joy,
And give us wings.

Belly's Got A Bike

Belly's got a bicycle
She rides it up and down
In and out the windows
And all around the town

And when she gets a puncture,
She mends it with a rope,
And pumps it up with dreaming
And fills it up with hope.

Lighter Than A Feather

Lighter than a feather, light as bright as white,
Bound up all together with the stars that shine at night.
The moon is not a mirror, but it does reflect the sun
And all the light around the world, reflects in everyone.

Yet still there are some places, that light has never been
Fish in deepest oceans, which the light has never seen.
And far off out in outer-space there's nothing light can hit,
So all the air seems dark as dark, as though it were unlit.

And I know yet another place, where there is light but none,
Inside this little head of mine, where all light is undone.
I close my eyes and I can see a world that's filled and right,
And every thought and memory is light as bright as white.

There are no windows in my head but eyes they let light in,
And then connect my optic nerve to where all lights begin.
So in my mind, although it's dark, I still see things so clear,
Which makes me wonder if it's true
And are they really here?

The things I see,
The things I see,
Inside my darkened head,
Why can I see them there at all,
And not just dark instead?

Mr Platypus

My friend the Duck-billed Platypus
He ate a great big cake,
And when he tried to swim again
He got a belly ache.

But by the time he'd managed,
To get back to the shore,
All that he could think about
Was cake and eating more.

So Platypus he bought a boat
And sailed it out to sea,
Where he had a lovely picnic
With his Duck-billed friends and me.

And when we'd eaten all the food
We had ourselves a sleep,
And I dreamed of sixty Platypodes,
All piled up in a heap.

I Grow And Grow

I know, I know and I will tell
How it is I grow so well...
I eat my fruit and eat my veg
And then jump on my garden hedge...

Yes I do lots of exercise
And don't eat chocolate box surprise,
Instead I eat some nuts and peas
And then I grow with strength and ease.

So big and strong
And well and fit
I grow and grow
And I love
It!

The Sloth

The sloth, the sloth, he is so slow
He takes an hour to move a toe,
So nobody can ever know,
Which way it is he wants to go.

The sloth, the sloth, such pretty eyes,
He's like a tree that's in disguise,
As still as still, just where he lies,
Eating leaves and watching flies.

The sloth, the sloth, that lovely face
He moves with elegance and grace
And keeps the very slowest pace,
He does not care who wins the race

The sloth, the sloth, is teaching me
That rushing round is not the key,
So just slow down and simply be
Like smiley sloth up in the tree.

I Am A Rolling River

I am a rolling river
I come from far away,
I've been flowing through this channel
Every night and every day.

With attrition and erosion
And abrasion, all so strong,
I make myself these banks and bed
That I keep rolling on.

Sometimes, when there's a confluence,
I meet up with a friend
As one we go meandering
Around bend after bend.
Deposition and an oxbow lake
We leave them far behind,
As we rush towards the estuary
The salty sea to find.

A stream and then a river
Until I reach the sea,
Where all the rivers of the world
Come down and swim with me.

Emily-Emily

Emily-Emily, sing me a song
Make it all happy and not very long
Make it about, all the stars in the sky
And all of the things, that I see with my eye.

Sing me a song about leopards and bears
Sing me a song about tables and chairs
Sing me a song about stars in the night
Sing of a walrus that's flying a kite.
Sing me a song about apples and cake
Sing me a song about learning to bake
Sing me a song about peacocks and tails
Sing about dolphins, riding on whales.
Sing about night-time, sing about day
Sing about children learning to play.

Emily sing me a song I can keep,
Dear Emily-Emily,
Sing me to sleep.

In Dad's Head

In dad's head there's a squeaking bat,
And a big bass drum,
And a musical cat.
There's a dog that plays on skin and bones,
With a pig that sings
On telephones.

There's an armadillo with a rusty flute,
And a herd of sheep
That howl and toot.
There's a goldfish that can play guitars,
And a tuba playing
Man from mars.

He's also got a noisy goat
With a saxophone
Stuck in its throat,
And a cow that plays the clavichord,
And a fox that whistles
When it's bored.

And if dad's snoring late at night,
These creatures give
My mum a fright,
When they all come marching
Down dad's nose
And dance in circles,
Round his toes.

Snails On Snow

Snails on snow,
Snails on snow,
They just don't know
Which way to go.
They slide around
And round and round,
Till tails and heads
Just can't be found.

Snails on ice,
Snails on ice,
They just can't listen
To advice.
They slip and slide
And glide and ride,
Across the icy
Countryside.

Yes,
Snails are better
In the sun,
Where they can walk
And they can run,
And they can stick
Their sticky shoe
Onto the earth
With
Gluey
Goo.

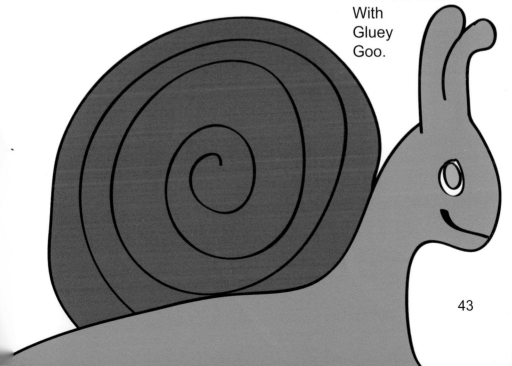

At Dad's Place

At dad's place we always know
What we're going to get to eat,
On Mondays we get sausages
Or baked beans for a treat.

On Tuesdays we get mustard,
On Wednesdays strawberry jam,
On Thursdays lumpy custard
With little strips of ham.

On Fridays we get roast beef,
On Saturdays bits of gum,
And on Sundays we all pack our bags
And hurry home to mum...

Photosynthesis

What is photosynthesis,
Apart from a long word?
It's really quite important,
For all the plants I've heard.

It's something about breathing,
And carbon dioxide,
But I don't really understand,
No matter how I've tried.

It's something about water
And sun and dark and leaves,
And something about oxygen
Which every plant it breathes.

In school my teacher told me,
(his name was Mr Rotten)
It's something about glucose,
But now I've quite forgotten.

So tell me something please
About a word as long as this,
I'd really like to know, you know,
What's photosynthesis?

The Witch's Soup

Jellied fruits and smelly boots
Are in the witch's soup,
And dirty ties
And buzzing flies
And stones from Cantaloupe.
I saw her spin
A badger in,
And fifteen squealing mice,
And dirty pants,
And fifty ants,
And fifteen thousand lice,

And wiggling worms and tiny germs
And cut up frogs and snails
And bits of mud
From the Congo flood
And sliced up serpents' tails.
Loads of sand
From a dead man's hand,
And battery acid too,
And I think I saw
Behind the door
A cut up kangaroo...

Yes the witch is making supper,
But still I have no fear...
If I tidy up my room
Then mum will reappear.

A Ghost I Am

My heart is made of leather,
My head is made of sand,
My arms are put together,
With a strange elastic band.
And when I try to speak
I jumble up my words,
And all my thoughts they fly away
On the back of screeching birds.

I haven't got a place to sleep
I lie awake at night,
Or wander round your house alone
To give you all a fright.
I've got blue eyes like a fairy,
But I'm never, ever kind
I'm horrible, grey and scary
I'm the worst thing you could find.

When I am feeling hungry
I nibble children's toes
Or cut them off and mix them up
With the bogeys from my nose.
Yes I'm a ghost, a ghost I am
But I won't give you a fright,
Unless you suddenly wake up
In the middle of the night!

A Ring-a-Ding-a-Doo

Daddy's drinking coffee and mummy's gone to bed
Uncle Richard's got
A brand new monkey on his head.
Little brother Simon
Made a pancake in his shoe,
And everybody's dancing
In a Ring-a-Ding-a-Doo.

When the monkey balances, upon a pot of limes,
He scratches all the valances
And starts to speak in rhymes.
Then mummy blows some bubbles
While she dreams of Vindaloo,
And everybody's singing
In a Ring-a-Ding-a-Doo.

When the weather's dim, we skim up all the tides
And wait for Arthur Pickering
To come and give us rides.
Then uncle Richard whispers
To his brother's kangaroo
That everybody's happy
In a Ring-a-Ding-a-Doo.

When we get much older then we'll put ourselves to bed
And everyone will listen
To the things that we have said.
And Daddy will be patient
And mummy will be too,
And everyone will laugh about
A Ring-a-Ding-a-Doo.

The Longest Neck

The giraffe his neck
It is so long
That when he wants
To sing a song
It takes an hour
To come along
That neck,
That neck,
So very long.
And when he wants
To give a shout
It takes so long
To get it out
That he's forgotten
All about
The reason why,
He wished
To shout.

My Body And Myself

My body and myself
We are the best of friends.
Wherever body wants to go
Myself it that way sends.
If suddenly I want to run
My body it speeds up,
And if my body's thirsty,
I drink water,
From a cup.

When my body's hungry
I give it food to eat,
I always feed my body
With a healthy, tasty treat.
You know I think my body is
A special place to be,
When I'm good to my body,
Then my body's good to me.

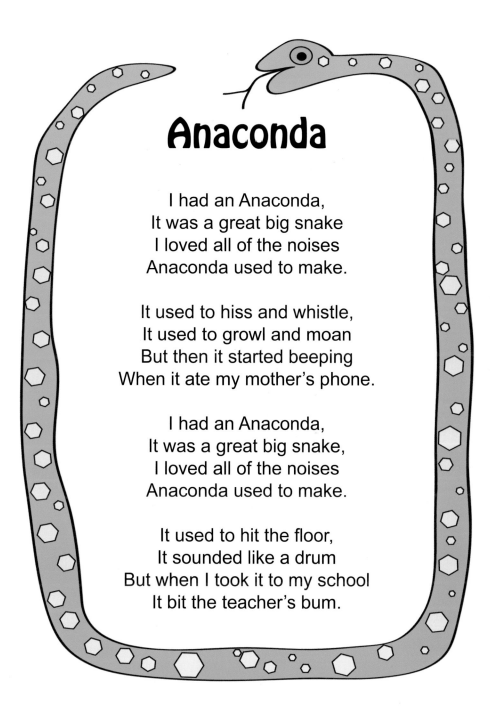

Anaconda

I had an Anaconda,
It was a great big snake
I loved all of the noises
Anaconda used to make.

It used to hiss and whistle,
It used to growl and moan
But then it started beeping
When it ate my mother's phone.

I had an Anaconda,
It was a great big snake,
I loved all of the noises
Anaconda used to make.

It used to hit the floor,
It sounded like a drum
But when I took it to my school
It bit the teacher's bum.

In Just A Little While

It's time for me to leave you now
It's time to say goodbye.
I've had such a lot of fun,
I almost want to cry.

It's time for me to leave you now
Though I don't want to go,
But thanks so much for having me,
It's been great fun you know.

So thanks for having me today
I hope I've made it clear,
That I would love to come again,
Perhaps this time next year?

So even though it's time to go
I'll sing a little tune,
For I'll be coming back to see you
Very, very soon.

Although it's time for me to leave
I'll be back in a while,
So don't feel bad, and don't feel sad
Just wave and give a smile.

Monsters Everywhere!

There are monsters in the garden
There are monsters in the shed,
There are monsters running everywhere
And jumping on the bed.

There are monsters in the kitchen
There are monsters in the bath,
There are monsters underneath the shed
And on the garden path.

There are monsters on the staircase
There are monsters in the hall.
There are monsters that are really big
And monsters that are small.

There are monsters that are orange
There are monsters that are pink.
There are monsters wearing perfume
There are some that really stink.

There are monsters that are purple,
There are monsters that are green.
There are monsters that are colours
That no one has ever seen.

There are monster that are friendly,
There are monsters that say "Boo!"
There are monsters eating daffodils
While sitting on the loo.

There are monsters!
There are monsters!
There are monsters everywhere!
There are monsters crawling on the ground
And floating in the air...

So I told mum what was happening
And she said she'd come and see
And then she walked around the house
Holding hands with me...

But when I tried to show her
All the monsters
It was weird..
Everywhere I took her to
They'd all just disappeared!

On The Mountain

From high up on the mountain
I walked across the land,
And swam across the lakes and seas
Out to the desert sand.
And there I met an old man,
As old as old can be,
Who leaned upon a walking stick
And said these things to me...

"What was it that you wanted
Do tell me like before,
Was it a bar of chocolate,
Or perhaps a dinosaur?
What was it that you wanted,
Please tell me right away,
Was it some peace and quiet,
Or perhaps a place to stay?"

As I rode on the river
And I rode on the stream
I saw the world pass by me
Like the shadow of a dream
And there I met a woman,
As old as old can be,
Who leaned upon a walking stick
And said these things to me...

"What was it that you wanted
Do tell me when you can,
Was it a thing that's lovable
Or just some marzipan?
What was it that you wanted,
Please tell me it's alright,
Was it a long and happy life
Or just to fly a kite?"

From high up on a mountain,
There flowed a tiny brook,
That ended in a fountain,
On the back page of a book.
And there I met a messenger,
Ten thousand years too old,
Who said that I should listen
To the story that he told...

That once there was a traveller
Who climbed a mountain high
Because he thought that he could reach
The middle of the sky.
And there he met an old man
As old as old can be,
Who whispered on a walking stick...
"What do you want from me?"

My Cousin Andy

My cousin Andy's got a six-foot nose,
And sixteen purple Pigeons
That whistle on his toes,
And when he goes to sleep at night
Twelve monkeys guard his bed,
And seven yellow spiders
Spin dreams around his head.

My cousin Andy's got a Chinese saw,
And a ticket from Mongolia,
In a book on Aztec law,
And when he swims out in the sea
He grows an orange tail
And makes a meal of sausages
In the belly of a whale.

My cousin Andy's got a bed that flies,
And a car that's made of marmalade
With forty-seven eyes,
And when he wrestles dinosaurs
I know he always wins
Because I read it in a letter
That he once sent to the twins.

My cousin Andy's got a sweet shop too,
And a gang of talking chipmunks,
And a pot of magic glue,
And when he sits up on the roof
He can name you all the stars,
And he says he's been to Pluto
And I know he's been to Mars.

Yes, my cousin Andy,
He's the best one in the world,
He's even got a little box
In which a snake is curled,
And daddy says that one fine day,
When he's saved up his money.
Then we're going to visit Andy
In the land of milk and honey.

The Monster Box

Inside the monster box
There are creatures rough and mean,
There's things that are much scarier
Than anyone's ever seen.
There's evil iguanas,
There's frogs the size of trees,
There's molten lava leprechauns
With dragons on their knees.

There's squirrels that were born in hell,
There's snakes the size of roads,
And diamond spotted liverquakes
That feed on poisoned toads.
There's munching, crunching Oggletoggs
That gobble children up,
And there's hairy spotted spiders
That are hiding in your cup.

When the monster box is open
All your nightmares come to life,
The gremlin's sharp and terrible teeth
They cut you like a knife.
And magic vines they tie you up
And hang you by your toes,
And burning fire beetle moths
Put earwigs in your nose.

And all the while you try to scream
But just can't make a sound
As stinging wasps they lock you up
In a box beneath the ground.
The monster box, the monster box,
So much bigger than it seems,
It looks quite small from outside,
But inside it's big as dreams.

I'd like to open up the box
And let these creatures out,
And then I'd like to watch you all
Run round and scream and shout.
But sadly, sadly, sadly
There's nothing I can do,
Although I'd like to scare the
Living daylights out of you.

Because when I left my house today
I found the monster box
(It was where I always keep it
In a bag of dirty socks.)
But sadly, sadly, sadly,
As sad as sad can be,
Although I found the monster box...
I couldn't find the key.

Nits!

No one in my family
Has ever once had nits.
What do you think that we all are
A bunch of stupid twits?
We do not go round the house,
Itching night and day...
If we had nits,
I tell you what,
We'd kill them right away...

If my dad thought that I had nits,
I bet he'd have some fun,
He'd get a pair of tweezers
And he'd grab them one by one.
My mum she'd get a hair dryer
And blow them all away,
My little sister wants a pet
She'd ask them all to stay.

Uncle Johnny he's a cleaner
And he'd know what to do,
If he found out that I had nits,
He'd flush me down the loo.
And my auntie she's a dentist,
(with very smelly breath),
If she was told that I had nits
She'd breathe them all to death.

No one in my family
Has ever once had nits.
What do you think that we all are
A bunch of stupid twits?
We do not go round the house,
Itching night and day...
If we had nits, I tell you what,
We'd kill them right away...

My Grandad, who's a policeman,
Says he'd lock them up in jail.
My brother says his rattle snake
Would swipe them with its tail.
Cousin Jenny, she's a baker,
And she's got a rolling pin,
She says that if she rolled my head
Those nits would soon give in.

Nanna likes to talk a lot
And eats ice cream in bed,
She says that if it's nits I've got
She'll lick them off my head.
I told her "That's disgusting."
Though she didn't seem to care,
But just as I had said it
I felt something in my hair...

I felt a little tickling
Right behind my ear,
And even though I scratched a bit
It wouldn't disappear.
It just kept moving round my head
It started at the top,
And then it went around the back
And still it wouldn't stop...

I got really, really itchy
On my left and on my right,
I was itchy in the afternoon
And itchier at night...
ITCHY ITCHY ITCHY!
SCRATCHY SCRATCHY
SCRATCH!

ITCHY-SCRATCHY,
ITCHY-SCRATCHY
SCRATCHY-ITCHY,
SCRATCH!

And still it just got worse and worse
(I was itching night and day),
Until mum and dad they saw it
And they hurried me away.
Then they took me to the barber,
And they sat me in a chair,
And then they told the barber man...
To cut off all my hair!

So now I've got no hair at all,
I'm bald as bald can be,
And the person in the mirror
Doesn't look a bit like me.
But one thing is for certain,
And one thing is for sure,
Those nasty little, scratchy nits
Won't itch me anymore.

I Hate Children!

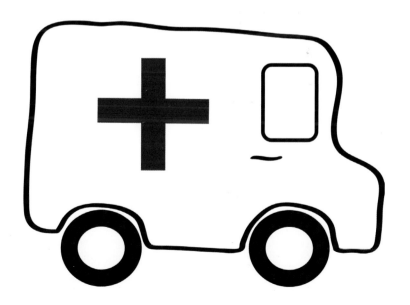

I hate children,
That's what the teacher said,
I wish I was on holiday
Or somewhere else instead.
I don't like all that smiling,
And I don't like silly games,
I don't like the way I have to learn
All of your stupid names.
So shut up and get working,
And just do what I say,
And if we're lucky,
We'll all make it
Out of here today.

FOCUS!

Arms down!
Back straight!
Eyes front!
Mouth shut!
Feet still!
Books out!
Don't move!

SILENCE!

I hate children,
That's what the teacher said,
You're just a bunch of little worms
With nothing in your head.
You know that if I had my way
You'd all be in the street,
Or sitting in a prison cell
With chains around your feet.
So shut up and get working,
And just do what I say,
And if we're lucky,
We'll all make it
Out of here today.

FOCUS!

Arms down!
Back straight!
Eyes front!
Mouth shut!
Feet still!
Books out!
Don't move!

SILENCE!

I hate children,
That's what the teacher said,
I wish that I was back at home
And still asleep in bed.
I hate all this teaching stuff
And trying to help you out,
I don't really care at all

I just like to **SHOUT!**
So shut up and get working,
And just do what I say,
And if we're lucky,
We'll all make it
Out of here today.

FOCUS!

Arms down!

Back straight!

Eyes front!

Mouth shut!

Feet still!

Books out!

Don't move!

SILENCE!

I hate children,
That's what the teacher said,
Then he just started shouting
And his face went really red,
And then he fell down on the floor
Pulling at his tie,
And his face it went
As red and round
As watermelon pie.

Then he went really quiet,
And we all gathered round,
And then his breathing nearly stopped
And he didn't make a sound.
Until little Charlie, at the back,
He stepped up and he said,
"You know what, you lot,
I really think,
The teacher might be dead..."

But the teacher opened up his eyes,
And he gave a little yelp
"...I didn't mean those things I said,
Please go and get some help..."
But we all just looked down at him,
He was a funny sight,
His face had gone from red to green
And then a greyish white.

Then Mary she stepped forward,
And she said right to his face,
"You're not a real teacher,
You're a horrible disgrace.
The proper teachers they're all kind
And they always help us out,
They try hard to explain things
And they never, ever shout.
They get us to enjoy our school
And they praise the good we've done,
And even though they're strict at times,
They're funny and they're fun...

But you, you're just a bully,
And we know you hate us all
And that's not fair because you're big
And we're still young and small.
You've made our lives a misery,
And I'll tell you something true,
The only thing that we all hate,
Is teachers just like you..."

Then we all sat down in silence
And when we heard the bell,
We told our favourite teachers
That the mean one was unwell...

And they all called an ambulance
And they took him out the door
And we never, ever,
Saw him
In a classroom
Anymore.

Up To You

That was it from me this time,
So now it's up to you.
Where do you want to go today?
What do you want to do?
Why not write a little verse
About something that you like,
About your favourite sandwiches
Or perhaps your favourite bike.

Why not write a poem that
Can make somebody smile?
Or one that makes them think a bit
For just a little while?
Or why not write a story
From whatever's in your head?
Or write a silly word or two
About something that you've read.

No matter what it is you write
I'm sure it will be good,
If you decide just what to say
And say it like you should.
So open up your head,
And then open up your mind,
And write a little something
About the strangest thing you find.

Where do you want to go today?
What do you want to do?
That was it from me this time,
The rest is up to you.

**Remember
to keep having fun with words.**

BORROWED BOOKS

Salve Factorem - Pax Possessori